This book belongs to

....

Front endpapers by Brooke Dowey aged 11 (left) and Samuel Robinson aged 7 (right)
Back endpapers by Adam Williams aged 10 (left) and Robyn Sharrocks aged 9 (right)

Thank you to Westgarth Primary School, Marske-by-the-Sea,
for all their help with the endpapers—K.P.

For Jac Duval–K.P.

OXFORD
UNIVERSITY PRESS

Great Clarendon Street, Oxford OX2 6DP

Oxford University Press is a department of the University of Oxford.
It furthers the University's objective of excellence in research, scholarship,
and education by publishing worldwide in

Oxford New York

Auckland Cape Town Dar es Salaam Hong Kong Karachi
Kuala Lumpur Madrid Melbourne Mexico City Nairobi
New Delhi Shanghai Taipei Toronto

With offices in
Argentina Austria Brazil Chile Czech Republic France Greece
Guatemala Hungary Italy Japan Poland Portugal Singapore
South Korea Switzerland Thailand Turkey Ukraine Vietnam

© Text copyright Oxford University Press 2013
© Illustrations copyright Korky Paul 1987, 1996, 1997, 2002,
2005, 2006, 2007, 2009, 2010, 2011, 2012, 2013
Based on books in the 'Winnie the Witch' series by Valerie Thomas and Korky Paul
The moral rights of the author and artist have been asserted

Database right Oxford University Press (maker)

First published 2013

British Library Cataloguing in Publication Data available

ISBN: 978-0-19-273537-9 (paperback)

2 4 6 8 10 9 7 5 3 1

Printed in China

Paper used in the production of this book is a natural, recyclable product made
from wood grown in sustainable forests. The manufacturing process conforms
to the environmental regulations of the country of origin

This is Korky Paul who draws the Winnie pictures.
How many times can you find him inside this book?

www.korkypaul.com

Valerie Thomas and Korky Paul

What Can You Spot in
Winnie's World?

OXFORD
UNIVERSITY PRESS

In the middle of winter there's a magical summer in Winnie's garden. It's very crowded, but can you spot . . .

★ two skulls? ★ two pirate hats?

★ two spotty hair bows? ★ a tennis racquet?

★ a red beastie? ★ a cat with an eyepatch?

★ a teddy bear wearing sunglasses?

★ a broomstick? ★ two green beasties' tails?

★ Winnie and Wilbur?

Phew! What a long queue at the museum. While Winnie and Wilbur are waiting with everyone to get in, can you spot . . .

⭐ a handstand? ⭐ two pairs of eyes in the roof? ⭐ a football?

⭐ a Winnie the Witch T-shirt? ⭐ a dinosaur skeleton?

⭐ a duck in a hurry? ⭐ a pair of roller skates? ⭐ a skateboard?

⭐ a bug sitting on a beak? ⭐ Winnie and Wilbur?

Winnie and Wilbur have just landed on the soft sand to spend a day at the seaside. Can you spot . . .

- ⭐ an orange crab? ⭐ a peg leg? ⭐ two flying flippers?
- ⭐ three wooden bats? ⭐ a witch with a yellow handbag?
- ⭐ a man buried in the sand? ⭐ a fishing rod catching a bikini?
- ⭐ a bird on top of a hat? ⭐ three long white beards?
- ⭐ Winnie and Wilbur?

Time for a pumpkin pit stop! While hungry witches
and wizards fill up their cauldrons, can you spot . . .

⭐ a wizard in yellow tights? ⭐ a wheel?

⭐ a pair of green socks? ⭐ two vampires?

⭐ four orange beasties? ⭐ two bare feet?

⭐ two ladies wearing glasses? ⭐ a witch who's
tripped over? ⭐ a snake in a cauldron?

⭐ Winnie and Wilbur?

Everyone is ready to draw a dinosaur! While all these people are painting their prehistoric pictures, can you spot . . .

⭐ a chef's hat? ⭐ five falling books? ⭐ two yellow eyes?

⭐ a purple lizard? ⭐ three pairs of glasses? ⭐ a boy on skates?

⭐ two stripy T-shirts? ⭐ someone carrying bones?

⭐ two yellow ears? ⭐ Winnie and Wilbur?

Winnie and Wilbur are in the spotlight!
Before the show is over, can you spot . . .

- a witch selling wands?
- a dropped ice cream? ⭐ a tentacle?
- two bare feet? ⭐ a fishing rod?
- a trodden-on tail? ⭐ a lost hat?
- a witch with three wands?
- a flower in someone's hair?
- Winnie and Wilbur?

Happy Birthday, Winnie!
All sorts of people have come to her party. Can you spot ...
a beastie with a bunch of flowers? four wizards wearing hats?
a cat costume? four crowns? two long white beards?
a mouse costume? four balloons? two pirates waving
cutlasses? three people lying down? Winnie and Wilbur?

Travelling by broomstick can be dangerous! While Winnie and Wilbur get back in the saddle, can you spot . . .

★ five stone faces? ★ a paper aeroplane? ★ a picture of Wilbur?

★ a basket of bread?

★ a scarecrow? ★ two bridges?

★ a yellow car? ★ a swimming pool? ★ two palm trees?

★ Winnie and Wilbur?

Winnie and Wilbur think it's wonderful underneath the ocean waves. Can you spot . . . a jellyfish? an octopus? a fish eating another fish? three shells? a fish sticking out its tongue? a turtle? four pairs of eyes in the darkness? two swordfish? six propeller blades? Winnie and Wilbur?

The sky is full of interesting things.
Sometimes Winnie and Wilbur stay up
all night. While Winnie uses her telescope,
can you spot . . .

⭐ four pairs of eyes in the darkness?
⭐ an unlucky worm? ⭐ two spaceships?
⭐ an owl? ⭐ two purple books?
⭐ a ladder? ⭐ Winnie's knickers?
⭐ five hats? ⭐ a dripping tap?
⭐ Winnie and Wilbur?

Ssshh! Winnie and Wilbur are fast asleep. Can you spot . . .
⭐ a green beastie? ⭐ five butterflies? ⭐ a satellite
dish? ⭐ a cat that isn't Wilbur? ⭐ a broomstick?
⭐ a pumpkin computer? ⭐ a spider's web? ⭐ eleven
books? ⭐ three odd socks? ⭐ Winnie and Wilbur?

Winnie the Witch lives in a black house in the forest. For your final challenge, can you spot . . .

⭐ a television? ⭐ a kettle?
⭐ a broomstick in a bedroom?
⭐ an indoor staircase?
⭐ a treasure chest with a curved lid? ⭐ two witchy portraits? ⭐ an odd shoe?
⭐ the smallest window in the house? ⭐ a toilet?
⭐ Winnie and Wilbur?